FINAL HECATOMB

Final Hecatomb

ALDIVAN TORRES

Canary Of Joy

Contents

1

Final Hecatomb

Final Hecatomb
Aldivan Torres

Aldivan Torres is a writer consolidated in several genres. So far, the titles have been published in dozens of languages. From an early age, he was always a lover of the art of writing, having consolidated a professional career from the second half of 2013.

He hopes, with his writings, to contribute to international culture, awakening the pleasure of reading in those who do not have the habit. Your mission is to win the hearts of each of your readers. In addition to literature, its main amusements are music, travel, friends, family, and the pleasure of life itself. "For literature, equality, fraternity, justice, dignity, and honor of the human being always" is its motto.

Final Hecatomb
Mountain cabin- night
Kitchen-cabin
Episode 3
Episode 4
Hecatomb 5
Episode 6-Valley of the Ghosts
Episode 7- Final Hecatomb
Hecatomb Final 8
Ultimate Hecatomb 9

Mountain cabin- night

Fortune-teller

I have arrived, my beloved friends. A force brought me here. Any news?

Guardian

Yes, lots of news. I am the force that has called you here. The reason is that the earth is in danger because of supernatural forces. They plan something bad. With that, our future is uncertain.

Renato

We need to react and avoid the worst. We need to find a way out and survive. We need to preserve the world for future generations.

Fortune-teller

I understand correctly. I agree with you. Furthermore, I took a long trip, and I am hungry. Have something to offer me?

Guardian

Yes, we have. Let's go into the cabin. That way, we can eat and talk better.

Kitchen

Guardian

All right, how long we haven't seen each other. How have you been, son of God?

Divine

I'm fine, with the same fights as usual. And you?

Guardian

I am guarding the mountain, taking care of my son and working on chores. I never stop.

Renato

I am studying and working with my mother. But what really amuses me are our adventures.

Divine

I imagine. I always appreciate your support. Furthermore, I really need this. My career has not been easy. I was born in a family of farmers and from an early age I faced misery, indifference, and prejudice. I grew up in a third-world atmosphere that crumbled my dreams with its cruel reality. But I had to resist at all costs. With contact with reading, my dream became a writer. However, I could not afford it. With that, I had to give up my dreams several times. Hope was reborn when it learned of the cave of despair, a place where the impossible becomes possible. So, I packed my bag, climbed the mountain and found you. But that was just the beginning. I had to overcome the challenges, get into the cave and become the seer. Then began the project of this saga. Currently, I can say that I am having a good time. Despite countless rejections in the professional and personal fields, I continued with the certainty of victory. We are here to help the world. I will do my best to preserve my species.

Guardian

Excellent. Good thing you're willing. Come with me to the mysterious forest, a world of dreams and fantasy. This is the point where you can save the whole world.

Divine

That sounds interesting. Yes, let's go! I am ready for better or worse.

Renato

I'm ready too. When does the adventure begin?

Guardian

We will travel tomorrow. How about if we stayed on the terrace?

Divine

Great idea. I love to watch the stars.

Terrace

Guardian

What is the meaning of life to you, Divine?

Divine

We all have a mission. Love and forgive each other. If we

do this, we keep all the commandments, and we achieve happiness.

Renato

I cannot forgive. I am only human.

Divine

I understand, Renato. It's not easy at all. But I think to forgive is move on. In fact, there is no way to forget a betrayal.

Guardian

Exactly, my angel. Forget the bad times and move on. Keep the good things with you. This will help your evolution.

Divine

That's why we are on the planet. When we evolve, we can find God's face through His creatures.

Guardian

This is wonderful. Finding God is a priceless mystical experience. I believe we can also find it when we do charity, giving good advice, guiding the illiterate and blind, acting on social causes, any good action leads us to this fundamental encounter in our lives.

Renato

We also meet God in children, for theirs is the kingdom of heaven. We must exercise this purity at all times. To enter the kingdom of God, we have to be like children.

Divine

For this reason, dear Renato, few achieve the kingdom of heaven. What we see in the world today are depravity, betrayal, unloving, selfishness and criminality. The world is with its deteriorated values. With this, the evil advances more and more.

Guardian

This was written in the prophecies. We are nearing the " Final Hecatomb ".

Divine

What do I do? Can I fulfill the prophecies?

Guardian

As long as there is hope, we have to fight. Life is a gift that cannot be missed.

Divine

It's ok. If it doesn't have to be this way, I will fight.

Renato

Do you believe in destiny?

Divine

Yes, I believe. It is a powerful force that guides us in our walk. He leads our actions to fulfill our mission.

Renato

And who drives fate?

Divine

My spiritual father. He coordinates the entire universe.

Guardian

We have reached the exact point of the discussion. About being "The son of God". Isn't that the height of pretension?

Divine

If I called myself a child of God, I would have no glory. But it was the spirit that chose me and called me that. What does this mean in practice? It means the purity of my heart against human wickedness. In me, the world has its only chance for salvation. I am ready to face the " Final Hecatomb ".

Guardian

Good thing we have you by our side.

Renato

Your powers will be totally needed now. We have surpassed "the first Armageddon" and now we will face this new endeavor. I am very excited about this.

Divine

Me too, Renato. I expect many emotions and adventures. These are the main ingredients of our saga. Any recommendations, guardian?

Guardian

We have to be cautious immediately. We don't know who our opponent is and that makes the adventure even more distressing and dangerous. Let's follow your intuition. This is our biggest safe haven immediately.

Divine

Thank you for your trust. I promise not to disappoint them. I'll plan so that everything goes well. I am a great strategist.

Renato

We know that, my idol. That's why you were summoned. We are in good hands.

Guardian

I agree. We are in great hands. How about we go to sleep now?

Divine

I agree. I am exhausted of the trip.

Renato

So, let's go! Tomorrow will be a new day.

Kitchen-cabin

Guardian

Good morning, my children. Did you sleep well?

Renato

Yes, my mother. I had beautiful dreams of adventure.

Divine

I slept well too. It felt like I was at my house.

Guardian

Make yourself at home. We have been living together for so long that we are already mother and child.

Divine

Thank you for your consideration. The feeling is reciprocal. Returning to the subject of adventure, when will we go to the mysterious forest?

Guardian

In a little while we will travel. We need to act fast, but with caution. The future of the world depends on it.

Divine

What a great responsibility! I look forward to helping the world. I also love fantastic adventures.

Renato

We are two, mate.

Guardian

I also love the adventures of our saga. We are the most important team in the world. Let's keep making viewers dream.

Divine

So be it, master!

Guardian

The right time has come. Let's go searching for adventure!

Field

Divine

I can't walk anymore. Are we still far from the mysterious forest?

Guardian

We're close. I'm tired too. So, I suggested we stop.

Renato

It was a really good idea. We had been walking for hours. It's all very stressful. Any clues about what we'll find?

Guardian

As its name implies, it is a mystery. We know we are expected. We also know that there is a plot involving this. But the reasons and circumstances involved, we do not know.

Renato

I get it. What do you say, seer?

Divine

I see chaos and fear. Fate is getting us to the right point. This is a world in danger. They need us.

Renato

Interesting. So, let's go on this adventure together! Let's live these fantastic emotions.

Mysterious forest

Nostrald

Welcome to my world, outsiders. I was expecting you all.

Divine

Who are you? What is your name?

Nostrald

My name is Nostrald, I am a prophet. I am descended from the greatest prophet who ever lived. And you?

Divine

My name is Divine. Very nice to meet you.

Guardian

I am the guardian of the holy mountain. I came from the third world with my friends to help you. You can count on us.

Renato

I am Renato, key element of this team. You can count on me too.

Nostrald

Thank you for your kindness. Before they try to avoid the end of the world, you must be prepared. I will teach everything I have learned. I will reveal my secrets. The meaning of the centuries of Nostradamus.

Divine

Amazing! Was just what I needed to know.

Guardian

Good idea. With this knowledge, we can try to do something.

Renato

We are at your disposal.

Nostrald

So, let's start. Listen to the first century and interpret. "Sitting alone at night in secret study; it is placed on the brass tripod. A slight flame comes out of the emptiness and makes successful that which should not be believed in vain."

Renato

" Sitting alone at night in secret study". Would it be a wizard?

Guardian

"It is placed on the brass tripod." Would that be the loneliness of power?

Divine

A slight flame comes out of the emptiness and makes successful that which should not be believed in vain." Does it mean the return of Christ?

Nostrald

You are very smart. The century talks about the future. It is a message that Christianity has always wanted to hide. The biblical message of Jesus' return is nothing more than a message in a figurative sense. Jesus has returned as a man and is already with us. Secret studies deal with the wisdom that the messenger will bring. You have to meditate on each of your words. It is a lonely and adverse person to the social conventions. Like Jesus, he is humble and noble in heart. Those who hear his commandments can finally find the kingdom of heaven. Who has ears, listen?

Renato

Where is this new Jesus?

Nostrald

He is closer than we think. To know it, just examine its fruits. It is written that every tree bears good fruit, the tree is also good. So, judge for yourselves.

Renato

Understood.

Divine

We've got the message, master.

Guardian

Just to note that we are all brothers in Christ, we all have some of that divine light that blesses us. So, we are all messengers of peace.

Nostrald

Let's go to the second century: "The wand in the hand is placed in the middle of the tripod's legs. With water he sprinkles both the hem of his garment and his foot. A voice, fear: he trembles in his robes. Divine splendor; the god sits nearby.

Guardian

" The wand in the hand is placed in the middle of the tripod's legs. " Does it mean procession of the faithful in Christ?

Divine

" With water he sprinkles both the hem of his garment and his foot. " Jesus washes the apostles' feet and is bathed by Mary Magdalene.

Renato

" A voice, fear: he trembles in his robes." Period prior to the arrest of Christ?

Guardian

" Divine splendor ". The angels comfort Jesus.

Renato

" The god sits nearby." Death of Christ.

Nostrald

You guessed everything. You are good disciples. This century refers to the passion of Christ. Congratulations to all of you! That was easy. Now let's go to the next one: "When the litters are overturned by the whirlwind and faces are covered by cloaks, the new republic will be troubled by its people. At this time the reds and the whites will rule wrongly.

Divine

" When the litters are overturned by the whirlwind." Invention of the plane?

Renato

"Faces cover themselves with cloaks." Advance of Islam?

Guardian

The New Republic will have trouble for its people: There Whites and Reds will rule wrong. Political corruption in Brazil?

Nostrald

Exact. From the New Republic, Brazil became a den of corruption. Metaphorically, it is said that democracy is government of the people. But this does not happen in Brazil. Governments make their decisions to privilege elites and themselves.

Divine

Unfortunate. What can we do?

We

Try to choose better candidates.

Guardian

I'm tired. Can we come into your house?

Nostrald

Of course, yes. Stay the will. I'm tired too.

Guardian

Thank you. Come on, my children?

Renato

With pleasure, mom.

Divine

Great idea, Master.

Episode 3

Kitchen-house

Nostrald

You can feel free. The house is yours.

Divine

Thank you so much for your kindness. What's your training?

Nostrald

I will teach the century, and we will travel the world. That way, you will have good stories to tell.

Renato

What's in your world?

Nostrald

Dinosaurs, dragons, and fairies among other enchanted characters.

Renato

That is cool! I will like it very much.

Guardian

It will be a great pleasure to help you in your goal. In return, you will reveal your secrets. I see this as fair and very interesting.

Nostrald

Exactly, honey. The world has always wanted to know my secrets. Finally, the time has come.

Divine

First, let's get to know each other better. What reveals your personal side, Nostrald?

Nostrald

I grew up in this enchanted forest with the awareness of

who I was. I was the bearer of the secrets of Nostradamus, my ancestor. This made me study the occult sciences a lot. I strengthened my spirit and mind by becoming the second-greatest prophet of mankind. On the other hand, my pure spirit longed to do good. So, when I noticed your arrival, I made the decision to reveal everything.

Divine

For humanity, this was his best decision.

Nostrald

Truth, friend. There is also the question of the "Final Hecatomb," a plot that comes ever closer to us.

Renato

My God! The ultimate Hecatomb! Is it the end of the world?

Nostrald

We don't know, Renato. I only know that there is an invisible plot around us. When I realized that, I was desperate. So, I used my powers to draw you here. Your fame of adventurers travels the entire universe. You are the most respected team in the world. I feel safe alongside such fantastic heroes.

Guardian

Thank you for your consideration. I also noticed this strange movement in the universe. We need to come together and avoid a bigger catastrophe. We need to fight for our survival.

Nostrald

Depending on me, you can count on me.

Guardian

We know that, thanks for your trust and welcome.

Nostrald

Returning to the first subject, could you talk a little about yourself?

Guardian

I am the guardian of the mountain, an ancient figure. I helped in the birth of seer training him to overcome challenges. Furthermore, I was the guide at the crucial moment of your life. Since then, we are always together in adventures.

Renato

The meeting with the seer totally changed my life. He freed me from a wicked father who only beat me. I could then believe my dreams and participate in this wonderful series.

Divine

I was born in a family of farmers. Furthermore, I grew up living with misery, prejudice, and indifference. I got wonderful gifts, but the financial obstacle made my career difficult. Still, I never stopped dreaming. I am currently a writer in a dozen languages, a filmmaker and a composer. I am already a winner for overcoming misery. But my big goals are: Win an Oscar and the Nobel Prize for literature. If I can do it, I don't know. But I will pursue this dream throughout my artistic career.

Nostrald

Very well! Believe in your dreams. Nothing is impossible for the one who believes. I admire your resume. If the world is saved, it will be by your hands.

Divine

Sure, friend. I already have the whole strategy in mind. At the right time, you will know.

Nostrald

How nice. It's late! Let's all sleep! Tomorrow will be a new day.

Guardian

Great idea, mate!

Leaving home

Nostrald

Here begins our journey. I will show you my world and its importance. Only then will you be aware of what is at stake.

Renato

Let's go with you! We love fantastic journeys filled with prose, food, dangers, and fun.

Guardian

It will be an honor to accompany you. We know it is a beautiful and charming world.

Divine

We are ready.

Episode 4

In the forest

Nostrald

We arrived in the enchanted forest. Here comes a dear specimen of this world.

Divine

What a beautiful place. It reminds me a bit of the previous adventure.

Nostrald

They are twin worlds. This place brings the fantasy that each person lives in their most beautiful dreams.

I'm glad I'm making my dream come true.

Guardian

This is the example of our perseverance. Most people give up in face the first hurdle. This makes them unhappy and unhappy people. Live your dream, even if it seems impossible.

Nostrald

That's right, guardian. How about if we made a visit? I haven't seen my cousin in a while.

Divine

Feel free, brother.

Renato

We go with you; we love making friends.

Guardian

So, it's decided. Let's visit your cousin and find out what fate has in store for us.

EPISODE 5

Houseroom

Nostrald

Good morning, cousin. How long. I was passing by and decided to visit you.

Cousin

It is always a pleasure to receive you. I missed you too. Who are those who accompany you?

Nostrald

They are my friends. I called them here to help us avoid the end of the world. Remember the prophecy of the final Hecatomb?

Cousin

I remember that if nothing is done, everyone will perish. There is a secret plot involved in this, just not sure what it is.

Divine

That's why we are here to unravel this mystery. You are in good hands. Invite us for tea?

Cousin

Of course, yes. Let's go to the kitchen. There we can eat and talk better.

Kitchen

Nostrald

Cousin, what happened in that time?

Cousin

I'm getting better. After I lost my parents, things are not being easy. They were my support and reason for living. Losing them really shocked me.

Nostrald

I understand, cousin. I also felt sad about their death. I have no words to comfort you.

Divine

People do not die. They just change because the spirit remains. Have faith in it.

Cousin

Thanks for the support. I wanted to know more about you.

Divine

I am an artist innately. I am a filmmaker, writer, and composer. I live creating my stories and enchanting the world.

Renato

I am an independent young man who believes in freedom, justice, and equality. I am willing to learn more from you.

Guardian

I am an ancient spirit that protects the mountain. I am here to accompany my two pupils and assist them.

Cousin

Thanks for the explanations. I see you have a wonderful potential winner.

Divine

Thank you very much. Returning to the subject of adventure, how can you be prepared to meet the challenges?

Cousin

Centuries are the method of preparation. In it lies the deepest secrets of existence. So, let's start.

Nostrald

In the world will born a king, who will have little peace and a short life. At this time, the papacy will be lost, ruled to its greatest detriment.

Divine

Being a king is a lot of responsibility. If this one get corrupted, then your reign is at risk. It is the true lord of heaven who judges his actions, and his shortened life is due to his mistakes.

Guardian

Many people want peace, but forget that we ourselves build peace. How can I harvest wheat if I planted the chaff?

Renato

When the church supports irrational and perverse measures, it loses control over them. In this sense, the sense of the institution that is the love of neighbor is lost.

Cousin

After the perverse measures, are built dictatorial regimes whose citizens' rights are suppressed. It's up to each one to rebel and try to change it.

Nostrald

Excellent, friends. This century can refer to King Felipe Iv of France.

Divine

I imagined it. This really is very intriguing.

Nostrald

Let's go to the next challenge. "They will be chased away and sent for a long fight. The countryside will be grievously boring. City and country will have greater struggle. Carcas-sonne and Nar-bonne will have their hearts tempted.

Guardian

Would be the harbinger of a world war?

Renato

With the wars and destruction, the

interior will be the quietest place.

Divine

The fights will be concentrated in large, populous and strategic areas.

Cousin

The temptations will be many on both sides. We must persevere in the faith.

Nostrald

This is all related. This refers to the end times, where the Christian church will be harshly persecuted. Let's look at the next message: Ravenna's eye will be abandoned, when his wings will fail at his feet. Bresse's two will have made a constitution for Turin and Vercelli that the

Frenchman will
trample.

Guardian

False friendship
leaves you at the
moment of your fall.

Renato

Great joints will
fail in the pursuit of
peace.

Divine

The constitution
is the voice of the
oppressed people.
This goes against
the powerful.

Cousin

The result is that
the people disman-
tle oppressive
movements. This is
called democracy.

Nostrald

This was the
French Revolution
that influenced
many other freedom
movements in the
world. We have
learned that fighting

for our rights is the best way to achieve peace.

Divine

What is the next topic?

Nostrald

The execution made,

The contrary wind, letters on the way home: The conjured XIIII of a sect, Rousseau companies shall expire.

Guardian

He handed his children to the orphanage but showed to be an advocate for children's education.

Renato

It fit into according to the economic situation. When money is short, it changes girlfriends.

Divine

It defended a libertarian system where man was totally integrated with nature. It was necessary to escape the corruption of society.

Cousin

With theories inapplicable to everyday life, his words fall into disrepute. He took refuge in his spiritual retreat, trying to understand the meaning of existence.

Nostrald

Very well. This legendary figure is named Jean-Jacques Rousseau, a leading philosopher of antiquity. Your thoughts have an influence on the world until now. Congratulations on your explanations.

The conversation was very helpful. That's it for today. Let's get on with our journey.

Hecatomb 5

forest

Nostrald

We arrived at the dinosaur valley. Here comes one of our specimens.

Divine

Oh my god!

Guardian

Oh my god!

Renato

Oh my god!

Guardian

This means that the dinosaurs did survive and the history of extinction is a fraud.

Nostrald

Yes, dinosaurs have survived in many worlds. But now not only are they at risk but the entire population of the earth.

Divine

It reminds me of a dream I had. I saw the earth being invaded by powerful creatures. It seems that there are already some among us. Can this be considered distressing?

Nostrald

Completely terrifying. We do not know what these extraterrestrials are capable of. So, my idea was to call you here. Perhaps your brilliant mind will free us from this mess.

Renato

My God! Who can save us? Is it the end?

Guardian

Calm down, Renato. We are on the side of the most enlightened being in the universe. Our beloved Son of God.

Divine

She is right. Trust me. I can do all things in him who strengthens me. We are the protagonists of this story and I promise a lot of excitement to our followers. Let's move on with faith.

Nostrald

What you're really capable of?

Divine

I am a great strategist. Throughout my life, I have faced many kinds of difficulties and I got over it. I had to survive and be happy anyway. Therefore, nothing shakes my faith.

Nostrald

You are an admirable master. It is well-deserved of success.

Divine

Thanks for the consideration, friend.

River

Nostrald

Are you enjoying the experience, Divine?

Divine

I'm loving it. It reminds me of so many stories.

Renato

I am very curious now.

Guardian

We are all reliable. If you wish, you can share your experiences with us.

Divine

Of course, yes. You are my friends. Despite the difficulties, my childhood was inspiring I grew up in Mimoso, alongside working countrymen and dreamers. I was just like any child. I played soccer, volleyball, swam in the river, studied, strolled, cared for animals, and worked in the fields. Although I had no money, I was happy and dreamy. I was just a child without responsibilities. This phase is the best of our lives. When we grow up, problems and troubles arise. You are bombarded with charges on all sides. If you fail, you are deemed incompetent. I say to you, fail as often as necessary to find your way. Cry as many times as necessary to be able to smile. Try as many times as necessary to be able to win. Anyway, be less demanding of yourself. That is the secret of success.

Nostrald

This fits exactly with the story of my life. Being a descendant of Nostradamus, the great prophet, people choked me with his demands. In response, I was dictating my pace of work. No one is born ready. We are the fruits of our choices that can lead us to happiness or unhappiness. I had the option to give up. I also had the option to insist. Choosing the second option made me the man I am today. A man who can give you cultural support in this journey.

Guardian

This also has importance in my career. I was appointed the protector of the Ororubá mountain and, in return, I obtained eternal life. My long existence has taught me the importance of work and perseverance. Each step in our lives is an important step to complete. How to build a house? First thing is to make a foundation. So, it is with all our projects. I tried, in my humble condition, to pass on some of my knowledge to my disciples. I think I was successful. Furthermore, I am proud to say that the seer is my main friend. Our meeting was instrumental in the creation of the seer series, the most important series in the world. Today, we have been working at the highest level of emotion, and we are part of the lives of many people who believe in our potential. We need to continue this work as far as God permits.

Renato

I understand you all. In my case, the biggest charging was from my father. I was even physically punished by him. Thank God I found angels who gave me the life I have today. Today, I have hopes. I want to graduate in law to be able to defend the cause of the poor.

Divine

What is the reason, Renato?

Renato

We are a country of inequality. To have quality food, health, and education we must pay for it. Is not fair. That should be everyone's right. We are all children of the same father. Why this difference?

Divine

This is the result of the economic system and corrupt governments. We can't change that. As long as there is a world, there will be inequality. We need to fight for what we believe in every situation. We need to do our part and make this world a little better.

Guardian

Generating jobs would be paramount to reducing inequality. But what we see are governments concerned with helping the rich at the expense of the poor.

Nostrald

This leads us to personal reflection and conclusion. You can't fix the world, but if we even take care of our lives, it will be a gigantic gain.

Divine

Truth. Each of these situations is part of our path. It is a tangle of events that demonstrates our character. That's why we are here. Here we can face the problem. This does not mean that we will be winners but just the fact that we try gives us credit. We are preparing for the "Final Hecatomb ".

Episode 6-Valley of the Ghosts

Nostrald

We arrived at the Valley of the Dragons.

Divine

Oh my god!

Renato

Oh my god!

Guardian

Oh my god!

Divine

We have walked for a long time. Any clues about the goal, master?

Nostrald

We're halfway there, and they haven't arrived yet. They must be investigating us. We have to be very calm at this time.

Divine

I understand. Glad we advanced. Let's get ready for the next steps.

Renato

What about the centuries? Will we learn more?

Nostrald

The training has been canceled because you already know enough. Now, let's move on to new knowledge. It will certainly be very fascinating things.

Renato

That is cool. We are ready to learn.

Divine

What do you see in our path, great master? How do you analyze our current moment?

Guardian

The future looks bright despite the alien threat. We all have capacity, and we are overcoming the obstacles. It is something similar to your mountain climbing. You had a dream, and risking your life became the only alternative at that time. By training the challenges, you have become capable of a fantastic turn: From a poor dreamer you have become a great seer, omniscient through your visions. From there began the series of adventures of the saga. In short, you have evolved as a human and professional being. The things are not easy. The paths are confusing and challenging. But do not worry. We are by your side as a motivation.

Divine

Great opinion. I am analyzing the whole situation before continuing. Thank you very much for your support.

Strange

My God! How terrible! I don't even believe it.

Nostrald

What is it, woman?

Strange

I saw a nasty animal destroying a crop. As he approached, he said that we all have the days numbered.

Renato

My God! What a terror! Didn't I say we are in danger?

Strange

What do you know about it? Can you explain it to me?

Divine

The earth is in danger. Powerful aliens plan to destroy us. We are trying to plan a reaction. We need to save the earth and all inhabitants, even if the cost is high.

Strange

Mercy! This looks like a horror movie.

Guardian

Calm down, woman. These are only assumptions. I believe we are still safe.

Strange

Are you confident, ma'am? Are the authorities hiding the real danger from us?

Nostrald

Well, we do not know. But even if we knew, we could do nothing. Aliens are super powerful and intelligent beings.

Guardian

The only one who can defend us is the son of God. He knows the secret. This can protect us from opponents.

Divine

I have the secret kept with me. At the right time, this will save us. I am the only one on earth capable of this. There is still hope. Believe me.

Strange

I feel more at ease. Be cautious, friends. You don't know who you're messing with.

Desert city

Nostrald

This is the light city, capital of the desert of my world. It is a great safe haven for travelers.

Divine

It seems charming to me!

Guardian

City of my dreams. Let's enjoy and eat somewhere?

Renato

I think it is a great idea. I'm starving.

Restaurant

Divine

It is a really long and exhausting walk. It is as if we are wandering. This is totally exciting and distressing. Any word of comfort?

Guardian

We have already had enough gains. At each point we pass, it is a new encounter. We know that we are approaching the truth. We are getting stronger and stronger. This is good news. Whatever awaits us, we are well-prepared. I am optimistic.

Divine

I am also very excited. Just going on vacation took me out of the daily monotony. I found you and a descendant of Nostradamus. I am learning a lot from all of you and enriching my saga.

Nostrald

I appreciate the part that it's up to me. It's also been very intriguing to me. Getting to know the most powerful team in the world is priceless. I am pleased with you and hope to contribute even more to the adventure.

Renato

Each experience adds us good vibes. It is critical for me to participate in all adventures. All this, it's healing my deepest aches. Thank you all!

Divine

Very well. Let's move on, then.

Episode 7- Final Hecatomb

forest

Ghost

Welcome to the valley of ghosts, outsiders.

Guardian

Really? It gives me the creeps. Simply amazing.

Divine

We are ready. Nothing can hurt us.

Renato

Do you mean you're a ghost?

Ghost

Exactly, my dear.

Nostrald

Do you allow us to cross the valley?

Ghost

What are you doing here?

Divine

We came to try to save the world. Powerful aliens plan to invade the earth, and we need to prepare for it.

Ghost

I understand. If it's for a good cause, you can continue your journey. I will give all my support.

Guardian

Thank you. What's your name?

Ghost

Edward. And yours?

Guardian

Spirit of the mountain. We come from the Third World.

Ghost

Very cool. I'm cheering for you.

Renato

Could you tell a little of your story?

Ghost

Of course, yes. It will be a pleasure. I came from the Third World. I came willing to achieve my goals by coming here. Furthermore, I was a very ambitious young man at the time. My dream was to become powerful and desired. I heard that in the valley of ghosts there were many riches, and so I went to get them. Arriving here, I traveled the whole valley, but unsuccessfully. I died of hunger, thirst, and cold. So, I became the keeper of the valley. I have been here for centuries, protecting the place and paying my sins. Only a millennium from now, my spirit will be free.

Nostrald

Very well. Each one reaps what he sows For God, there is no eternal penalty. You will be able to overcome this and return to the realm of light.

Ghost

I hope so, friend. Until this time comes, I will continue to fulfill my mission with dignity.

Guardian

We're rooting. Your efforts will be rewarded.

Ghost

I wish the same to you. Do not disappoint us. Our future depends on your action. We need to survive at any cost.

Gypsy Village

Nostrald

Good morning, we arrived just now. Could you let us know where we are?

Gypsy

Very welcome. You are in the gypsy village. I am the site manager.

Renato

Are we close to completing the route?

Nostrald

We completed three quarters of the way. From here, the danger begins to increase.

Renato

Thank you for the information.

Divine

Could you tell us something about the future?

Gypsy

Who am I before the mighty seer? But if you are curious, I can help. You are an example of dedication and struggle. Day after day, I see your efforts pursuing your dreams. It is truly an example for so many young people. In your case, the following saying applies: Whoever sows, reaps. Sooner or later, the great sun will shine upon you and your victory will come. On this day, all uncertainties will be erased. You will enter a new phase of prosperity, success, and love.

Divine

My God, how wonderful. Do I deserve all these blessings?

Gypsy

You deserve it because you are a Being of Light. I guess what goes around comes. Keep seeking the kingdom of God, and all other things will be added.

Renato

I was curious now. Could you say something about me?

Gypsy

With pleasure, Renato. You come at a growing pace in the personal and professional area. You are assertive and hardworking. Your projects are possible eventually. For this, your focus should be on strategic planning, fault correction and perseverance. I see an open path to adventures, emotions, learning, and achievements. You will be a full being.

Renato

It's great to know that. Since childhood, I have many projects. The seer's example inspired me to continue with my dreams. I don't know exactly when it's going to happen, I just know it's worth having faith in a larger force. This force guides us in the darkness of disappointment. I promise I will always believe and try hard for my goals. I am already a winner.

Gypsy

That's the spirit. All the luck in the world to you.

Nostrald

What can we do to succeed in this endeavor?

Gypsy

You are already doing everything right. No wonder you are considered the most competent team in the world. Your fame has spread throughout the universe as heroes of the planet.

Nostrald

I appreciate the support. It is good to know that we are on track. Each learning shows us our continuous evolution, and despite the danger we are in, we are very focused. Every detail is important on this journey.

Guardian

It's been a great opportunity to get to know each other better. Each of us has a contribution to the saga. A project that started ten years ago. Following the poor boy from northeastern Brazil who became a filmmaker is really rewarding. He teaches us every day the true values of an honest man. He is our beloved symbol of victory over hardship.

Divine

Thank you, Master. I owe all my success to you and my followers. Let's get on with the journey. There is so much for us to discover in this fantastic universe.

Hecatomb Final 8

Night forest

Nostrald

Why do you cry, miss?

Hindi

I'm living a complicated family time. I'm the housekeeper while my sisters live their life at parties. As I work, life goes by. You know, I'm very young and wanted to build a life. I wanted to get married, have my children and have fewer responsibilities. However, nobody supports me. I need help. I can't handle all this pressure.

Renato

What is your name?

Cindi

Cindi. And yours?

Renato

Renato. Look, I know well what's going on. Since my mother died, I've been alone with my father. He beat me and made me work twelve hours a day. It was a very difficult time when I wished for my death. That's when I decided to run away. Along the way, I found the support of the guardian and my dear seer. Without them, I wouldn't be here today. That is why I advise you to consider the possibilities before making a final decision.

Cindi

You're right, Renato. You are an intelligent young man.

Guardian

Haven't thought about reacting yet? How do you handle all this?

Cindi

I have no way out. My mother and father died. My sisters and stepmother remained. I have no affinity with them. I am simply despised and treated as mere garbage.

Guardian

I understand. It is a really complicated situation. But do not lose hope. Maybe your enchanted prince to show up and changes this story.

Cindi

I lost my hopes. For boys, I am only a garbage worthless. It is really depressing.

Divine

I don't see you as a poor thing. I see a determined young woman. Stop blaming others for your problems. Act instead of thinking. When you take the reins of your life, things will happen.

Cindi

Who are you? A philosopher?

Divine

I am the essence of God. I came down from heaven to rescue the oppressed poor. Through my example, I seek to encourage people.

Cindi

Your example? What do you mean?

Renato

He is the farmer who became a world-famous filmmaker.

Nostrald

He is the seer, a superpowered being through his visions.

Guardian

He is the lead artist in the "The Seer" series, the most prestigious series in the world.

Cindi

My God. What an honor to meet you here in the middle of the forest. This place is called "The Valley of the Repressed" which concentrates all my suffering. This can change? What is your story? I really need to know her.

Divine

I am from northeastern Brazil, a pocket of misery from the Third World. Born in a repressive environment, I had to fight for my dreams hard. With each failure, I wondered if there was any chance of success because my dreams were almost impossible in the face of my reality. It was my faith in a greater force that guided me all the time. Pursuing my dream, I suffered over three hundred rejections in the personal and professional fields. Everything was very distressing. But I am overcoming the obstacles little by little. Today, I am a writer published in more than a dozen languages and award-winning filmmaker. Although I have not achieved all my goals, I can say that it is worth fighting for what we believe. Winning, or losing, is a reason to live. Returning to your question, everything can change under the skies. Just believe and do conscious planning.

Cindi

What a wonderful story. You are an inspiration to those who dream. Now, I'm just curious. What brought you to my world?

Divine

We have come to try to avoid the end of the world.

Cindi

End of the world? What do you mean? Can anyone explain me?

Nostrald

We are being victims of a conspiracy. Powerful aliens plan to take over the world.

Cindi

Aliens? My God, how terrible! I thought I had seen completely.

Guardian

Yeah, friend. We are trying to react. We need to survive anyway.

Cindi

I want to avoid dying! Please help us.

Renato

Calm down, miss. God is by our side. He is enlightening us on our way. Have faith!

Cindi

It's ok. I will have all the faith in the world. How to find happiness? What counsel do you give me, prophet?

Divine

Don't call me a prophet. I am just a dreamer. If I had to give advice, I'd say: Live your leading role in the theater of life. When we assume responsibility for our actions, we are proactive. We take the risks of mistakes and hits. This is very brave. We have to blame ourselves less and act more. We have to believe in ourselves. Gather all your dreams and focus on them. Focus on what is critical to you. As we set priorities, the chances of victory increase considerably. But remember that the path of honesty is not an easy one. You will encounter difficult obstacles along the way that will serve as learning. This is where most give up. Be part of the minority and persist. In the future, it will reap the due fruits. Who sows, reaps?

Cindi

Thank you so much for the words. I wish you every success in the world on your journey. Please, save the world!

Ultimate Hecatomb 9

Night cabin exterior

Peter

Welcome, outsiders. What brings you here in my beautiful, magical forest?

Nostrald

We are seeking to defend the world. I don't know if you know, but we are in imminent danger.

Peter

Do you refer to the aliens?

Nostrald

Exactly. They are everywhere.

Guardian

What's your name?

Peter

Peter. I am the protector of the forest and of the humble. And you?

Guardian

Spirit of the mountain. We are here to help you all. It is part of our mission to engage in social actions.

Peter

Very generous of you. I really am in a wonderful moment. There are aliens everywhere. I don't know what they are up to.

Renato

We deduce that it is an invasion. They intend to take over the planet and eradicate the human species. We need to avoid this at all costs.

Peter

It is a reasonable suspicion. So, we need to act while it's still time.

Divine

It is already late. I am hungry and cold. Could you invite us for a snack at your house?

Peter

Of course, yes. Sorry for my unkindness. The trip must have been a long one. Come to my cabin. I will take care of you with all affection. We took advantage of the occasion and get to know each other.

Divine

Thank you so much for this.

Kitchen

Guardian

There are only two phases left to reach the final goal. Getting here is a reward for our efforts. We replay our trajectory in the mind as if we were in a movie. I conclude that I regret nothing. Peter, thank you for your good hospitality. Could you talk about your work here in the magic forest?

Peter

No need to thank. I always welcome everyone. Regarding my work, I am a social architect. The magic forest is a very unequal world. There is the poor, the servant, and the monarchy. Of all these, the least privileged is the poor. My role is to redistribute income. I take money from the rich and give it to the poor.

Renato

But wouldn't that be theft?

Peter

Not at all, friend. The poor are already robbed from birth. I just do it justice. With this attitude, I am sought in every kingdom. Good thing I have the protection of the forest spirits. No one can arrest me.

Renato

It's all right! Forgive me if I offended you.

Peter

It was nothing.

Divine

It's very brave of you. But I don't know if it solves the problem. I believe that inequality is a problem without a solution. This is the result of the economy regime adopted by the government. It is up to each one to find his place in the sun.

Peter

Well, it was the only way out I found. I could not mourn or be without action at this. Right or wrong, no one can judge me.

Divine

I know that. The only one who judges are God.

Peter

I am flattered by your understanding. You look like a nice guy. I see a light around you. You are predestined to be pleased.

Divine

Hopefully, friend. My life has not been easy for me. I have been walking along twisting paths during my thirty-six years of life. I know I still have much to conquer and fight. A force guides me toward my destiny.

Nostrald

Always believe in yourself, Divine. We own our destiny. I am with you on this adventure, and for better or worse.

Divine

Thank you. Without you, I'm nothing.

Renato

What is life like in the magic forest?

Peter

Despite the inequalities, life in the magic forest is very dynamic. From the simplest to the most important, everyone has a function. I seek to help every species in my world, and they repay with their friendship. Doing good is very noble for my part. This also contributes to my evolution.

Renato

That is cool! Very interesting indeed.

Guardian

Why this name? Magic forest?

Peter

It's a long story. But I will summarize for you. Legend has it that it was because of the fairy dispute. Because of the power struggle, there were intense spiritual battles. That's why the place became known as magical. With the growth of the forest, the name adopted was "Magic Forest ".

Guardian

Excellent. Knowledge is always important to reflect on history.

Nostrald

What you plan for the future?

Peter

I want to continue on this same path. I know I've already contributed a lot. I hope to help my fellow men even more.

Nostrald

Wonderful. Furthermore, I admire beings of light.

Peter

I do no more than my obligation, friend. When are you leaving?

Divine

Today. I take the opportunity to thank all your affection and support, but the mission calls us. Thank you so much for everything!

Guardian

You do an impressive job, and it's very cool. Success and keep on rooting for us.

Renato

You have changed my thinking. I am grateful for that.

Nostrald

Loved the food. Now I am stronger to be able to continue.

Peter

I thank you. Go in peace and may God bless you.

The aliens have finally arrived. I've prepared a surprise for them.

Guardian

We're saved. How can we thank you?

Divine

No need to thank me. It was an honor to have helped my species. Let's move on and perpetuate the species.

Renato

You're my idol! I knew you'd save us. It's time we went home.

Nostrald

I say goodbye to you with your heads held high. I know I contributed somehow to this success.

Divine

Of course, your help was fundamental to our victory. By the way, I thank you all. This isn't goodbye. It's a long time! Let the next adventure come.

The aliens have finally arrived. I prepared a surprise for them.

Guardian

We are saved. How can we thank you?

Divine

No need to thank. It was an honor to have helped my species. Let's move on and perpetuate the species.

Renato

You are my idol! I knew you'd save us. It's time to go home.

Nostrald

I say goodbye to you with your head held high. I know I contributed in some way to this success.

Divine

Your help was critical to our victory. By the way, thank you all. This is not goodbye. See you soon! Bring on the next adventure!

The End

9 786599 556265